Prairie Christmas

Prairie Christmas

by

PAUL ENGLE

LONGMANS, GREEN AND CO.

NEW YORK · LONDON · TORONTO

1960

LONGMANS, GREEN AND CO., INC.
119 WEST 40TH STREET, NEW YORK 18

LONGMANS, GREEN AND CO., LTD.
6 & 7 CLIFFORD STREET, LONDON W 1

LONGMANS, GREEN AND CO.
20 CRANFIELD ROAD, TORONTO 16

PRAIRIE CHRISTMAS

PUBLISHED SIMULTANEOUSLY IN THE DOMINION OF CANADA BY
LONGMANS, GREEN AND CO., TORONTO

FIRST EDITION

LIBRARY OF CONGRESS CATALOG CARD NUMBER 60-53226

Printed in the United States of America

A Christmas Child

Hearing about those winter nights
When Mary traveled to that place
And had her Child, our own child's face
Illuminates the Christmas lights.
She shudders with that desert cold,
As if she, also, huddled there
When the Child breathed its first live air,
Eternally but one day old.

I'd help, she cries, I'd give my coat,
The one that's trimmed with rabbit fur,
My muff and mittens. As her throat
Pulses in pride and love, the wild
And mortal childhood lies in her
Praises that calm, immortal Child.

Contents

Contents

Prairie Christmas

I

An Iowa Christmas

Every Christmas should begin with the sound of bells, and when I was a child mine always did. But they were sleigh bells, not church bells, for we lived in a part of Cedar Rapids, Iowa, where there were no churches. My bells were on my father's team of horses as he drove up to our horse-headed hitching post with the bobsled that would take us to celebrate Christmas on the family farm ten miles out in the country. My father would bring the team down Fifth Avenue at a smart trot, flicking his whip over the horses' rumps and making the bells double their light, thin jangling over the snow, whose radiance threw back a brilliance like the sound of bells.

There are no such departures any more: the whole family piling into the bobsled with a foot of golden oat straw to lie in and heavy buffalo robes to lie under, the horses stamping the soft snow, and at every motion of their hoofs the bells jingling, jingling. My father sat there with the reins firmly held, wearing a long coat made from the hide of a favorite family horse, the deep chestnut color still glowing, his mittens also from the same hide. It always troubled me as a boy of eight that the horses had so indifferent a view of their late friend appearing as a warm overcoat on the back of the man who put the iron bit in their mouths.

There are no streets like those any more: the snow sensibly left on the road for the sake of sleighs and easy travel. We could hop off and ride the heavy runners as they made their hissing, tearing sound over the packed snow. And along the streets we met other horses, so that we moved from one set of bells to another, from the tiny tinkle of the individual bells on the shafts to the silvery, leaping sound of the long strands hung over the harness. There would be an occasional brass-mounted automobile laboring on its narrow tires and as often as not pulled up the slippery hills by a horse, and we would pass it with a triumphant shout for an awkward nuisance which was obviously not here to stay.

The country road ran through a landscape of little hills and shallow valleys and heavy groves of timber, including one of great towering black walnut trees which were all cut down a year later to be made into gunstocks for the First World War. The great moment was when we left the road and turned up the long lane on the farm. It ran through fields where watermelons were always planted in the summer because of the fine sandy soil, and I could go out and break one open to see its Christmas colors of green skin and red inside. My grandfather had been given some of that farm as bounty land for service as a cavalryman in the Civil War.

Near the low house on the hill, with oaks on one side and apple trees on the other, my father would stand up, flourish his whip, and bring the bobsled right up to the door of the house with a burst of speed.

There are no such arrivals any more: the harness bells ringing and clashing, the horses whinnying at the horses in the barn and receiving a great, trumpeting whinny in reply, the dogs leaping into the bobsled and burrowing under the buffalo robes, a squawking from the hen house, a yelling of "Whoa, whoa," at the excited horses, boy and girl cousins howling around the bobsled, and the descent into the snow with the Christmas basket carried by my mother.

While my mother and sisters went into the house, the team was unhitched and taken to the barn, to be covered with blankets and given a little grain. That winter odor of a barn is a wonderfully complex one, rich and warm and utterly unlike the smell of the same barn in summer: the body heat of many animals weighing a thousand pounds and more; pigs in one corner making their dark, brown-sounding grunts; milk cattle still nuzzling the manger for wisps of hay; horses eying the newcomers and rolling their deep, oval eyes white; oats, hay, and straw tangy still with the live August sunlight; the manure steaming; the sharp odor of leather harness rubbed with neat's-foot oil to keep it supple; the molasses-sweet odor of ensilage in the silo where the fodder was almost fermenting. It is a smell from strong and living things, and my father always said it was the secret of health, that it scoured out a man's lungs; and he would stand there, breathing deeply, one hand on a horse's rump, watching the steam come out from under the blankets as the team cooled down from their rapid trot up the lane. It gave him a better appetite, he argued, than plain fresh air, which was thin and had no body to it.

A barn with cattle and horses is the place to begin Christmas; after all, that's where the original event happened, and that same smell was the first air that the Christ Child breathed.

By the time we reached the house my mother and sisters were wearing aprons and busying in the kitchen, as red-faced as the women who had been there all morning. The kitchen was the biggest room in the house and all family life save sleeping went on there. My uncle even had a couch along one wall where he napped and where the children lay when they were ill. The kitchen range was a tremendous black and gleaming one called a Smoke Eater, with pans bubbling over the holes above the firebox and a reservoir of hot water at the side, lined with dull copper, from which my uncle would dip a basin of water and shave above the sink, turning his lathered face now and then to drop a remark into the women's talk, waving his straight-edged razor as if it were a threat to make them believe him. My job was to go to the woodpile out back and keep the fire burning, splitting the chunks of oak and hickory, watching how cleanly the ax went through the tough wood.

It was a handmade Christmas. The tree came from down in the grove, and on it were many paper ornaments made by my cousins, as well as beautiful ones brought from the Black Forest, where the family had originally lived. There were popcorn balls, from corn planted on the sunny slope next the watermelons, paper

horns with homemade candy, and apples from the orchard. The gifts tended to be hand-knit socks, or wool
ties, or fancy crocheted "yokes" for nightgowns, tatted
collars for blouses, doilies with fancy flower patterns for
tables, tidies for chairs, and once I received a brilliantly
polished cow horn with a cavalryman crudely but
bravely carved on it. And there would usually be a
cornhusk doll, perhaps with a prune or walnut for a
face, and a gay dress of an old corset-cover scrap with
its ribbons still bright. And there were real candles
burning with real flames, every guest sniffing the air for
the smell of scorching pine needles. No electrically lit
tree has the warm and primitive presence of a tree with
a crown of living fires over it, suggesting whatever true
flame Joseph may have kindled on that original cold
night.

There are no dinners like that any more: every item
from the farm itself, with no deep-freezer, no car for
driving into town for packaged food. The pies had been
baked the day before, pumpkin, apple, and mince; as
we ate them, we could look out the window and see
the cornfield where the pumpkins grew, the trees from
which the apples were picked. There was cottage cheese,
with the dripping bags of curds still hanging from the
cold cellar ceiling. The bread had been baked that morning, heating up the oven for the meat, and as my aunt
hurried by I could smell in her apron the freshest of all
odors with which the human nose is honored—bread
straight from the oven. There would be a huge brown
crock of beans with smoked pork from the hog butch-
ered every November. We would see, beyond the crock,

the broad black iron kettle in a corner of the barnyard, turned upside down, the innocent hogs stopping to scratch on it.

There would be every form of preserve: wild grape from the vines in the grove, crabapple jelly, wild blackberry and tame raspberry, strawberry from the bed in the garden, sweet and sour pickles with dill from the edge of the lane where it grew wild, pickles from the rind of the same watermelon we had cooled in the tank at the milkhouse and eaten on a hot September afternoon.

Cut into the slope of the hill behind the house, with a little door of its own, was the vegetable cellar, from which came carrots, turnips, cabbages, potatoes, squash. Sometimes my scared cousins were sent there for punishment, to sit in darkness and meditate on their sins; but never on Christmas Day. For days after such an ordeal they could not endure biting into a carrot.

And of course there was the traditional sauerkraut, with flecks of caraway seed. I remember one Christmas Day, when a ten-gallon crock of it in the basement, with a stone weighting down the lid, had blown up, driving the stone against the floor of the parlor, and my uncle had exclaimed, "Good God, the piano's fallen through the floor."

All the meat was from the home place too. Most useful of all, the goose—the very one which had chased me the summer before, hissing and darting out its bill at the end of its curving neck like a feathered snake. Here was the universal bird of an older Christmas: its down was plucked, washed, and hung in bags in the barn to be put into pillows; its awkward body was roasted until the skin was crisp as a fine paper; and the grease from its carcass was melted down, a little camphor added, and rubbed on the chests of coughing children. We ate, slept on, and wore that goose.

I was blessed as a child with a remote uncle from the nearest railroad town, Uncle Ben, who was admiringly referred to as a "railroad man," working the run into Omaha. Ben had been to Chicago; just often enough, as his wife Minnie said with a sniff in her voice, "to ruin the fool, not often enough to teach him anything useful." Ben refused to eat fowl in any form, and as a Christmas token a little pork roast would be put in the oven just for him, always referred to by the hurrying ladies in the kitchen as "Ben's chunk." Ben would make frequent trips to the milkhouse, returning each time a little redder in the face, usually with one of the men toward whom he had jerked his head. It was not many years before I came to associate Ben's remarkably fruity breath not only with the mince pie, but with the jug I found sunk in the bottom of the cooling tank with a stone tied to its neck. He was a romantic person in my life for his constant travels and for that dignifying term "railroad man," so much more impressive than farmer or lawyer. Yet now I see that he was a short man with a fine natural shyness, giving us knives and guns because he had no children of his own.

And of course the trimmings were from the farm too: the hickory nut cake made with nuts gathered in the grove after the first frost and hulled out by my cousins with yellowed hands; the black walnut cookies,

sweeter than any taste; the fudge with butternuts crowd-
ing it. In the mornings we would be given a hammer,
a flatiron, and a bowl of nuts to crack and pick out for
the homemade ice cream.

And there was the orchard beyond the kitchen window, the Wealthy, the Russet, the Wolf with its giant-
sized fruit, and an apple romantically called the North-
ern Spy as if it were a suspicious character out of the
Civil War.

All families had their special Christmas food. Ours
was called Dutch Bread, made from a dough halfway
between bread and cake, stuffed with citron and every
sort of nut from the farm—hazel, black walnut, hickory,
butternut. A little round one was always baked for me
in a Clabber Girl baking soda can, and my last act on
Christmas Eve was to put it by the tree so that Santa
Claus would find it and have a snack—after all, he'd
come a long, cold way to our house. And every Christmas morning he would have eaten it. My aunt made
the same Dutch Bread and we smeared over it the same
butter she had been churning from their own Jersey
(highest butterfat content) milk that same morning.

To eat in the same room where food is cooked—that
is the way to thank the Lord for His abundance. The
long table, with its different levels where additions had
been made for the small fry, ran the length of the
kitchen. The air was heavy with odors not only of food
on plates but of the act of cooking itself, along with
the metallic smell of heated iron from the hard-working
Smoke Eater, and the whole stove offered us its yet
uneaten prospects of more goose and untouched pies.

To see the giblet gravy made and poured into a gravy boat, which had painted on its sides winter scenes of boys sliding and deer bounding over snow, is the surest way to overeat its swimming richness.

The warning for Christmas dinner was always an order to go to the milkhouse for cream, where we skimmed from the cooling pans of fresh milk the cream which had the same golden color as the flanks of the Jersey cows which had given it. The last deed before eating was grinding the coffee beans in the little mill, adding that exotic odor to the more native ones of goose and spiced pumpkin pie. Then all would sit at the table and my uncle would ask the grace, sometimes in German, but later, for the benefit of us ignorant children, in English:

> *Come, Lord Jesus, be our guest,*
> *Share this food that you have blessed.*

There are no blessings like that any more: every scrap of food for which my uncle had asked the blessing was the result of his own hard work. What he took to the Lord for Him to make holy was the plain substance that an Iowa farm could produce in an average year with decent rainfall and proper plowing and manure.

The first act of dedication on such a Christmas was to the occasion which had begun it, thanks to the Child of a pastoral couple who no doubt knew a good deal about rainfall and grass and the fattening of animals. The second act of dedication was to the ceremony of eating. My aunt kept a turmoil of food circulating, and to refuse any of it was somehow to violate the elevated nature of the day. We were there not only to celebrate a fortunate event for mankind but also to recognize that suffering is the natural lot of men—and to consume the length and breadth of that meal was to suffer! But we all faced the ordeal with courage. Uncle Ben would let out his belt—a fancy western belt with steer heads and silver buckle—with a snap and a sigh. The women managed better by always getting up from the table and trotting to the kitchen sink or the Smoke Eater or outdoors for some item left in the cold. The men sat there grimly enduring the glory of their appetites.

After dinner, late in the afternoon, the women would make despairing gestures toward the dirty dishes and scoop up hot water from the reservoir at the side of the range. The men would go to the barn and look after the livestock. My older cousin would take his new .22 rifle and stalk out across the pasture with the remark, "I saw that fox just now looking for his Christmas goose." Or sleds would be dragged out and we would slide in a long snake, feet hooked into the sled behind, down the hill and across the westward sloping fields into the sunset. Bones would be thrown to dogs, suet tied in the oak trees for the juncos and winter-defying chickadees, a saucer of skimmed milk set out for the cats, daintily and disgustedly picking their padded feet through the snow, and crumbs scattered on a bird feeder where already the crimson cardinals would be dropping out of the sky like blood. Then back to the house for a final warming up before leaving.

There was usually a song around the tree before we were all bundled up, many thanks all around for gifts, the basket as loaded as when it came, more so, for left-over food had been piled in it. My father and uncle would have brought up the team from the barn and hooked them into the double shafts of the bobsled, and we would all go out into the freezing air of early evening.

On the way to the door I would walk under a photo-graph of my grandfather, his cavalry saber hung over it (I had once sneaked it down from the wall and in a burst of gallantry had killed a mouse with it behind the corncrib). With his long white beard he looked like one of the prophets in Hurlbut's illustrated *Story of the Bible*, and it was years before I discovered that as a young man he had not been off fighting the Philis-tines but the painted Sioux. It was hard to think of that gentle man, whose family had left Germany in protest over military service, swinging that deadly blade and yelling in a cavalry charge. But he had done just that, in some hard realization that sometimes the way to have peace and a quiet life on a modest farm was to go off and fight for them.

And now those bells again as the horses, impatient from their long standing in the barn, stamped and shook their harness, my father holding them back with a soft clucking in his throat and a hard pull on the reins. The smell of wood smoke flavoring the air in our noses, the cousins shivering with cold, "Good-bye, good-bye," called out from everyone, and the bobsled would move off, creaking over the frost-brittle snow. All of us, my mother included, would dig down in the straw and pull the buffalo robes up to our chins. As the horses settled into a steady trot, the bells gently chiming in their rhythmical beat, we would fall half asleep, the hiss of the runners comforting. As we looked up at the night sky through half-closed eyelids, the constant bounce and swerve of the runners would seem to shake the little stars as if they would fall into our laps. But that one great star in the East never wavered. Nothing could shake it from the sky as we drifted home on Christmas.

II

A Handmade Christmas

That older Christmas was one we seemed to hold in our hands. After all, our hands seemed to create so much more of it then than now.

A few evenings before Christmas we would sit around big dishpans of popcorn, each child with a long thread and a needle, making strings of white corn to shine from branch to branch of the green tree. We had raised that corn ourselves in the garden behind the house. I had spent many hot mornings hoeing between the hills of corn, so that my feelings toward it were a little mixed. I always seemed to jab the kernels a lot harder than my sisters, so that the needle would break through and punch my skin. It was a miniature blood sacrifice, proper to that holiday which celebrated the birth, with its blood, of the God who would die in His blood.

There were also popcorn balls to be made just the size of baseballs, the sticky stuff shaped lovingly in our hands. The whole kitchen reeked of the crisp smell of corn and the sweet smell of hot syrup—and so did we.

We would wrap oval, pointed butternuts, from a

grove on the farm where my mother had been born, in sheets of tinfoil, tying them with string so that they could be hung from the tree, to have a second and more glittering life back again in mid-air.

This was before tree stands had become so elaborate. My brother and I would build a new frame out of boards every year, nailing together such a stout support as would outlast the needles themselves.

Of course, the greatest tree was the tall one at church on Christmas Eve, with its long candles wavering in the drafty air and a man standing at one side with a ten-foot pole which had a wet sponge tied on the end, ready to douse any fires that started. I fear that, along with the other children, we prayed as much for a really menacing fire to start as we did for the Christ Child. Once I was rapped smartly on the hand with that rod for trying to get an extra sack of candy passed out at the end of the service.

There was always a church play on Christmas Eve, given at great cost to bed sheets and tempers. I was usually an anonymous shepherd with instructions to keep my grating voice low so as not to interfere with those who could sing. However, the shepherds carried crooks, which we used with deadly effect to trip the ankles of the splendid characters who had been the saintly Joseph and the Wise Men a few minutes before. The star that led the Wise Men across the desert traveled on a wire across the tiny stage, and often stuck halfway across, long before it reached the corner which was the barn where Joseph and Mary and the Child lay. One of the shepherds would then lift his crook to the starry heavens and shove that wayward star over where it belonged, sometimes bringing down the skies themselves.

Many of the gifts were made right in the family. My older brother usually had some wooden object out of his manual training class, a stool, a rack for the kitchen wall, while my sisters were busy with elaborately scrolled initials in the corners of handkerchiefs or with aprons on which whole gardens of flowers were appliquéd. I was too small to make anything except mischief, but my ambition was to whittle as well as my uncle on the farm, who could make a whistle which would really blow, carve little animals out of soft pine, or a tiny rifle with a peep-sight. Nevertheless, I tried, and one year managed to chip and cut and beat a darning egg from a chunk of wood, sanding its awkward corners down, rubbing wax in until it was literally a handmade and hand-polished thing, wrapped in the fanciest paper I could find and presented to my mother as if it had been the Kohinoor diamond.

But was not Joseph, the father of Christ, a carpenter, and would he not have had a patient interest in a child's handwork out of wood?

It was our mother, of course, who made the most, something for every one of the four children, sewing late every night, hiding mysterious articles whenever one of us went through the little room off the kitchen where she had her sewing machine. By devotion, skill, and loss of sleep they would be finished and wrapped handsomely under the tree, the shirt, the coat, the dress, when we came down on Christmas morning.

Many years, going reluctantly to bed on Christmas Eve, hanging over the stair railing for a last hope of seeing, if not Santa Claus himself then at least a late-working mailman with a package, the last sound we heard would be that sewing machine. It was the old foot-powered Singer, whirring on into the late night on a final hem, resembling my mother in its strength for work, its steadiness, the cheerful sound it made. If I heard that treadle going tonight I would look across the room for a tree with candles and look out the window for a drift of snow with its blue shadow. Most of all, I would want to hear it stop, to be followed by my mother's hurrying, bright steps going from sewing machine to Christmas tree with the last packages, weary but eager, the floor creaking as the house turned cold. That plain machine noise brings back our tears, our childhood, and our life.

It was also a mechanical noise that wakened us on Christmas morning, that angry but comforting sound which was my father shaking the cast-iron grates in our coal furnace. It was pleasant to burrow down in the covers knowing that in a few minutes, after that banging and shoveling had stopped, a little heat would creep timidly out of the hot-air registers. We had one register in the floor between two rooms and always hung a red paper bell over it, so that when the heat was really flowing up the bell would toss and sway in its silent ringing.

We made the paper cones that hung on the tree, and filled them with candy my sisters had boiled and poured and whipped in the kitchen. My reward for cracking the nuts we had gathered in gunny sacks after first frost on the farm (and for not eating all that I cracked) was scraping the pans. Somehow, the bits and dribblings I knocked loose tasted better than the beautiful neat squares on their trays. This did not keep me from steal-ing a few solid pieces when my sisters were not looking. Since the candy had been made for a solemn holiday, my beginning conscience would give me a bad time when I considered that I was actually at the start of a life of crime as a thief. This period of soul-searching usually lasted as long as it took my hand to lift up and snatch the candy. At that point I managed to beat down my spindly moral sense and to beat a fast retreat to another room, where I could contemplate my wicked-ness while eating the spoils.

The Bible has many references to caves, places where prophets lived, where Christ was taken after the Cruci-fixion. We had our own cave right in the house, a little closet with a miniature door. We could use it for play most of the year, hiding in it and scaring ourselves by closing the door and sitting in the dreadful dark. Weeks before Christmas, however, we had strict orders never to enter that closet, as it was my mother's hiding place for gifts. We would walk by, knowing that a quick pull on the door would reveal all the forbidden treasure, but somehow we realized the hallowed nature of the place, and not one of us ever looked. In the last few days before Christmas my mother would make many trips there with the presents she had made, and each trip made that odd place, which existed only because of a carpenter's error, a more secret and sacred cave.

Because my father's business was horses, he would have to go on Christmas morning to feed and water them. Since Christ was born among animals, He would have understood this sort of work, even when it had to be done on His own holiday. At noon my father would drive up in his red-and-green sleigh to tie his horse to our hitching post, where the iron-headed horse stared back at the living one. I would run out and help him buckle a warm blanket around the horse. There is no sound any more like sleigh bells making their muffled jingle-jangle under a wool blanket when a horse shakes and stomps. There would also be whinnyings when other horses trotted by with their own bells clanging their cold and echoing sound.

After we had eaten our dinner, it would be my job and my excitement to give the horse his nose bag of oats. This I could only do, being so small, if the horse put his head down, so that I could fasten the strap over it. That was easy, because I would sneak a piece of Christmas candy, let the horse sniff it, and then lower it until I could throw the strap over. (Today I would be named a compulsive candy thief and the dangerous flaw in my personality cause for a visit to a psychiatrist to find out what wickedness I was expressing by this sweet debauchery. I have grown a little taller since then, but have I conquered my vice? Never ask.) I can still hear the grinding of those big horse teeth in the feed bag and the clash of the bells when he would toss his head back to reach the last oats at the bottom. I can see the steam coming from his nostrils, flared and pink, and see, too, my own face reflected, complete and tiny, in his glowing brown eyes. To relate publicly, in the best modern manner, the real depth of my depravity, I must admit that I managed to lower the horse's head, in order to take off the feed bag, with still another piece of stolen candy. It is more than the freezing air of the season that causes me to shake at the thought.

It was a handmade Christmas. The entire family either sewed, whittled, knit, sawed, nailed, crocheted (just try to pronounce *that* word the way it is spelled in English), embroidered, baked, pasted, or cracked to celebrate that generous Day with gifts. There was one object, however, which we made just for ourselves, the star for the top of the tree, cutting it from a stiff piece of cardboard. My job, as a zealous collecter of leadfoil (like any one hundred per cent real American boy on his way to being President), was to produce some large sheets of the heavy stuff, not yet rolled into a ball to be sold by weight. This I did without revealing my sources of supply, as some of my brightest pieces smelled strongly of Horseshoe plug, and our aunt Minnie considered nicotine an instrument of the devil.

We would wrap the star in my best leadfoil and tie it on the highest point of the tree, where it could reflect the wavering wax candlelight, a handmade star, more wonderful to us than any in the sky because we had actually held it in our hands.

Not only was Christmas more personal then, it was also more exotic. We are all accustomed now to food and clothing brought to us from across America and from around the world, but when I was a child the things we ate and wore were much more local.

The tree itself, fir, pine, spruce (romantically called *evergreen*), was far outside the Iowa landscape, where elm, maple, oak lost their leaves each autumn as, it seemed to me, regular trees should. But these shipped in for Christmas were so strange it was as if they might have come from that far country where the birthday of the Child we were celebrating had taken place. It was exciting to look at the rows of evergreens suddenly appearing along the sidewalks in what is so expressively called the dead of winter. It was curious to go up and touch their hard shininess and smell their tang out of remote forests. In Iowa green was the color of pastures in June, of young corn, of new oats and hay, of living crops. Coming as they did in December, the Christmas trees brought a sense of the beginning of life, exactly at the time when our own landscape seemed to have no life in it at all.

What really brought the renewal of life to a child was the setting up of that tree in the house, its decorating, and then the magical moment when the true candles were lit and the whole green and romantic structure was covered with little, living flames. I was luckier then, in a wooden house in a small Iowa city, than the Child Himself, who had in all His childhood no such glittering thing to anticipate each year.

There were many other foreign-seeming objects in our Christmas. While I sat by the tree with a wet sponge on a long rod, in case the tree caught fire from a candle (half hoping it would, and yet half fearful), all the children had a pile of exotic, once-a-year nuts. There were pecans, almonds and Brazil nuts, remarkable and unreal when compared to the hazel and hickory and butternuts from the farm. But most different of all was the "English" walnut. Our Iowa black walnut was a rugged thing, which stained our hands yellow-brown in gathering and had a shell so tough it had to be beaten with a hammer on a flatiron (which we used to call a sadiron). These English walnuts, however, had fragile shells which my brother could crush in his hands, and meats which, while sweet, lacked the oily richness of our native black walnuts. It took brute strength to break through to the meat of our own kind, but the reward was a tastier and solider one.

We all hung our stockings from a table on which the tree stood, and every Christmas morning found in the toe a fresh orange, the only one we were sure of getting all year, for it was not a time when fruit traveled as gaily around the country as it does now. The orange, like the English walnut and the evergreen tree itself, came to our hands with a sense of distance about it. Surely that feeling is gone for children now, when they see oranges all the year round and weary of being told to drink their juice. We savored our orange section by slow section, and rubbed the aromatic skin on our noses, and felt in its orange-colored sweetness something of the far-off country of Palestine, a place famous for its oranges.

Although wiser heads have assured me that the orange may have come from Florida, the walnut from California, and the pine tree from Minnesota, and although my geography has expanded to include other continents, if not other stars, when all these objects come together at Christmas I still have a child's shock of being very close to the original village of Bethlehem in the desert where the first instant of the Christian Era began.

Like all decent Iowans, we had cousins in California who sent us boxes with pictures of palm trees, clusters of raisins, Chinese baskets with dragons circling them so that they scorched their own tails with the fire from their mouths. These also gave an exotic flavor to the season. It enchanted me to discover that branches of our own family lived in places which might be, to judge by the articles we received, not far from Judea, the fruit-growing country where that celebrated birth occurred. In the confusion of my mind at five years old the vast Iowa picnic at Los Angeles (and the very name of the city itself) became associated with the holiday and gave me a sense of participating in a great ceremony thousands of miles away. Later I was disillusioned, but for some years it gave me a powerful satisfaction to think that, through my cousins, I shared in that place and that event.

Perhaps the most exotic, and certainly the most exciting, object to come from far away was the annual huge box of candy from my uncle George, who had gone west as a young man and set up a candy store near the Blackfoot Indian reservation in Idaho. He always included in his package a box of chocolates labeled "fancy," hand-dipped, with a "gold" spoon tied to the top by an orchid ribbon. The cover bore a full length portrait of a scantily clad beauty, bold enough to stand there almost naked, but shy enough to turn slightly away from us all too eager viewers. This caused a certain amount of soul-searching among the more pious members of the family, who nevertheless always managed to eat a good share of the chocolates. Aunt Minnie simply ignored the daring young girl and looked on the cover as a landscape, commenting on what a nice waterfall that was.

So we made our Christmas, partly with our hands, partly with strange-seeming things long since become familiar. We scattered thimble cookies under the tree for any Brownies who happened to be passing by that night. There must have been a lot of them on the move, because by morning the little cookies would all be gone. We went to bed knowing that we had made such gifts as each child could at his own age, knowing that the whir of the sewing machine meant that our mother was still sewing on her own last gifts, and knowing that in the morning there would be a shining star on the tip of the Christmas tree, because we had shaped it ourselves and hung it there, long years before these new times in which men are trying to hang their new metallic stars in space. Will they have such hope and joy in their clever machines as we had, creeping reluctantly off to bed, in our plain star, silvery with leadfoil and reeking richly of that tobacco which Aunt Minnie fought with barehanded gallantry? We knew that in the morning she would come by and say, "Your tree always has such a pretty star."

She stood there in a collar she had crocheted for herself, and we said nothing, for in her deceived innocence she was a part of the simple goodness of the times. With our hands we had made a part of her Christmas, as we had made a part of our own.

II

With the excitement of the Great Day in our minds, it was always a gamble whether we would wake up and be running downstairs before our parents had gone to bed. Some nights they must have had very little sleep as they worked late finishing gifts and arranging them under the tree. We had a rule, however, as my mother said it, "No getting up while it's dark, but any time after it starts to get light." I fear that our idea of light on a freezing December morning was the dimmest touch of gray at the edge of a heavy sky.

Once down, we were allowed to have the wax candles lit on the tree, so that we opened our gifts under flickering lights and with the resinous tang of scorched pine needles in the air. We opened our packages in order, the youngest first, so that all of us had a share in every gift. Always there were the useful things we needed to wear, delayed until they could be counted as a part of Christmas, the products of that busy sewing machine, dresses for my sisters, shirts for my brother and me. Every year we all received mittens connected by a long cord to run through the sleeves of our coats so they would not be lost.

There were the wonderful presents, too, my brother's first watch, found in the toe of his stocking, thick, with a big stem for winding and a place inside the back cover where one day he would have a tiny picture. Held up to the candlelight, it seemed more radiant than jewels or the gay sun itself, just beginning to shine through the window.

There was also my older sister's last doll, the largest yet, with hair the color of her own, and a set of doll clothes my mother had made in imitation of my sister's own dresses and coats. I remember a tiny tam-o'-shanter, brilliant red, worn at an angle over the doll's long curls with such devastating effect that I yearned for such a treasure and in the following weeks secretly picked up that doll and held it.

Our stockings would be filled with little presents and with candy, that hard kind with designs of flowers, and no matter how hard you licked it and how small the piece became, the flower remained whole to the end. We had long arguments about the question of stockings, whether each of us should hang one he actually wore or whether we had a right to hang the largest we could find. Naturally, the smallest children were bitter at the idea of hanging their own narrow stockings, and glorious were the years when we found our father's long, heavy socks for high boots. We hung them in triumph, like Sioux hanging scalps. We wore them around our necks when we were greased for a sore throat, and later when they were worn out our mother would use them for dusting.

This was the only time during the year when we were given books. I would lay my hands on the hard package as if the story of Buffalo Bill, or the honest young man in Horatio Alger, or the song-sounding stanzas of Stevenson's *A Child's Garden of Verses*, could break through the paper and rush up the tips of my fingers.

By now other children would be pouring in from around the neighborhood to admire our presents and invite us over to look at theirs. The grimmest Christmas of my childhood was the one on which an electric train was delivered to the boy next door *by mistake*, and no one ever came back for it. As if fallen from heaven, it stood under their tree in its big box, untouched until they were certain it would stay unclaimed. Even after we had set it up in his attic, that train had a fine air of illegality, almost of sin, making it more fun to play with than any other boy's train which had been properly bought.

By midmorning we would be back home helping prepare for the invasion of relatives at noon. We had to clear the living room of its chaos, wrapping paper, boxes, string, seals, gifts lost in the confusion. But the really important work was in the kitchen. The cookstove had been heating up for hours, thanks in part to many trips I made for that greatest of all quick-burning fuels, corncobs, of which we had a great pile in the back yard. Our range would roar when we gave it a little draft. It made an impressive sound of cooking, giving off growls and threats at the pots and pans, warning them to start cooking or suffer for it. Somehow our silent modern cooking seems unreal and unfair, as if the heat sneaked up on the food without fair warning.

The first food preparations had, of course, been made months before. There were cookies with nuts, raisins and spices, piled in an earthenware crock and put in the basement to age. There were green peppers stuffed with cabbage and put in crocks of brine. There were sweet pickles which, while cooking, had a penny thrown into the kettle so they would turn bright green. There were crocks of mincemeat with green tomatoes and currants. All these crocks were a fine earth-gray color. They stood on shelves in the cellar, with towels tied over the top so that mice would not fall in and drown. It was my job to bring these up the steep stairway, holding each crock under my nose so that I could breathe in the special, rich odor of each, the dill picked in the hot August sun, the cabbages cut just before frost in early October.

The finest flavor of all came from the spiced apples, which had lengths of real cinnamon in their jars. As a reward for trudging up and down the stairs I would be allowed to take out a stick of cinnamon, dripping with apple juice and tasting of spices I could not name. This I would suck, making it last all day. Sitting by the kitchen range, hearing it mumble and grumble to itself as the split oak felt the fire's bite, sleepy from the short night, the morning's excitement, the loaded errands, I would close my eyes and lick the melting richness of that dark-brown bark. No shop or restaurant in this wicked world today has such deep delights.

On the back of the stove would be a pan of dried corn into which cream had been poured. It would bubble and chuckle back there, pleased at having all that moisture once stolen from it replaced by so fine and golden a liquid as my uncle's Jersey cows produced.

There would be the fancy, sweet, once-a-year things with the elegant names: *ambrosia*, fruit and ginger ale and coconut, foreign-tasting and handsome; *divinity* fudge, which took praying over so it would be the right consistency; *fondant*, kneaded in the hands, wrapped in a damp cloth so it would not crystallize. The loveliest in my greedy eyes was the hickory nut cake. I had given a lot of my life to that small object. After frost I had gathered the little nuts from trees on my uncles' farms and lugged them home in a sack, spreading them out on a porch roof to dry. Then I had cracked what seemed like millions but was probably only thousands, mashing my fingers on the flatiron where I held them for the hammer; then picking out the tiny bits of meat with a sharp nutpick which kept jabbing into my hand. I had literally bled for that cake, and in the end, one little piece on my plate seemed not to represent the anguish I had given.

Then we would hear a jangle of bells outside and a yelling of children as our cousins and their parents arrived, bobsled loaded with presents, with ducks in granite pans needing only to be heated. It was an abundant arrival. Food was in everyone's arms, carrots from the root cellar deep behind the house, apples from the russet tree in the orchard, a skinned and frozen rabbit terrifying me with its bloody, blue flesh. The clothes were ample, too. My aunt always had tremendous hats which only a strong back and a strong character could have kept poised in a winter wind. She was considered slightly frivolous for always wearing feathers in her hat. There was also a fox fur around her neck, the head glaring down at me in outrage at the sad end to which it had come.

Soon other relatives arrived, Uncle Ben of the big mustaches, the childless man who always said to me, "Let's see how big your chest is," and slipped a quarter into my shirt pocket. Ben would bring a jug of apple cider, "sweet," he would assure his wife Minnie, but, according to my father, it was "hard as rocks." Aunt Minnie always brought presents she had crocheted, knit, tatted, or embroidered. We all knew from the dismal feel of the package just what she was giving us. I usually received a crocheted necktie. Minnie had no children and only the most unreal notion of what boys were like, so that I usually received a pink tie which hung down to my knees. There were endless doilies, table runners, and initialed handkerchiefs. It was our conviction that on December 26 each year Aunt Minnie began manufacturing those endlessly appearing, superbly useless items.

Dinner was the sort of debauch which could be eaten only by men who had already done a morning's chores and would do an afternoon's, even on such a holiday. We ate with gentle brutality the beautiful ducks which the summer before I had chased into the pond with a wild flutter of wings and a monstrous quacking. We ate wild grape jelly, tart and bright in its bowl, made from clusters picked on the same vines where I would swing on summer visits to the farm. We ate wild plum preserves, from that sweetest of all fruit when ripened in the sun along a sandy road where bees and birds and an occasional horse are the only travelers. Aunt Minnie would bring a little jar of rose-hip jam, the eating of which was restricted to ceremonial nibblings.

The most trying part of dinner, however, was the grace that preceded it. My mother's uncle Jake had in his day been an amateur preacher, although now his closest public approach to the Almighty was in the rare occasions when he was invited to beg a blessing on our food. He must have felt that the deity was hard of hearing, as he always raised his deep baritone so that it rumbled through the house; if any human sound was capable of penetrating to heaven, it was the voice of Uncle Jake. He also felt that a brief blessing was unworthy of the food, and it was often a question as to whether my father, whose idea was that the Lord already knew how hard we had worked and how mightily we needed nourishment, would reach for his knife before Jake had finished. I noticed that when this happened, the prayer ended abruptly, Jake seized his own knife (I now think in self-defense) and assaulted his victuals as eagerly as the rest of us.

Afternoons we took our sleds (in my case, my brother's old one, repainted) and went sliding on those wonderful empty streets. We could slide six long city blocks downhill without risk of being maimed for life. The men of the family filled the air of our living room with cigar smoke. At the first sniff of nicotine, Aunt Minnie would flee the corrupt room and peer out of the kitchen like an enraged tiger from its cave. Minnie always won, for it was not long until the men had put down their cigars and dozed off, belts unbuckled.

There were two events in the evening. One was the

taffy pull, when we would wait for the last stirring of
the kettle in which molasses had been boiling, then take
the chewy stuff in our hands and run outside, to twist
and pull it as the night cold made it brittle.

The other event was the final tribute to the holiday.
We would gather around the melodeon, my mother
would start pumping it, air would begin moving
through the little bellows and the narrow reeds, and we
would sing from the book of Christmas songs published
in the nineties, my mother leading, Ben enthusiastically
off key, Jake full and proud, the children wailing thinly:

> *From the eastern mountains*
> *Pressing on they come,*
> *Wise men in their wisdom,*
> *To His humble home.*

In my simple view, His humble home might have been
the gingerbread house my mother had made. I could see
it sturdily sitting under the tree as I sang.

Then the children were marched off to bed. We
hated to let that Christmas go, for it had been a close and
family matter. We had put our strength into it, churning
butter, grinding coffee, kneading dough, whipping
cream with a hand beater, turning ice cream, making
things which are now not even worn, giving our energy
and getting back a quiet security. One Christmas I had
sent away for a book on taxidermy and had laboriously
stuffed a mouse, wiring it to sit up and beg with its piti-
ful little feet. This delicate object I had wrapped and
presented to Aunt Minnie with overwhelming pride as

my most cherished homemade thing. When she saw it, Minnie fell back onto a sofa with a mouselike squeak and a flutter of gray petticoats, the same cloth which turned up years later in a patchwork quilt of my mother's. It was a bond Minnie and I had forever.

The children would go to the kitchen, open the oven door (the range would still be hot, although no longer roaring) and each would take a heated flatiron wrapped in flannel. Then we would sadly go through the living room, where the relatives were still talking, say good night, and go off exhausted but still tense. "Watch that sadiron," Ben would yell at me, "it's a left-handed one." Obediently, I transferred it to my left hand, although it looked about the same to me in either hand. Ben would wink at me and inhale that cigar smoke which Aunt Minnie would not allow him to produce himself. Minnie would hold my hand in her strong and bony fingers and speed me to bed with the firm advice, "Merry Christmas. Avoid sin."

So we straggled off to the unheated bedrooms, putting our irons under the covers and our favorite present under our pillow (one time mine was ice skates which would clamp on shoes of any size; they don't make bad sleeping, under a duck-down pillow, if you are full of duck). I would run my hands over the many patches of cloth on the quilt that my mother had made, recognizing a smooth silk she had worn, a rough serge, a wool shirt I had outgrown. Our whole life was gathered in the scraps of that quilt.

My feet would feel around for the warm sadiron, working it up and down to warm the icy sheets. Downstairs I could hear the easy rumble of talk from the relatives, adults who also did not want to give up this marvelous, communicating day. Our cousins were already asleep on couches downstairs, taking the earned sleep of those who have split wood, who have built the fire to cook the duck that was their soft-feathered and absurd-voiced friend.

I would drift off to sleep curled around that cloth-wound and comforting iron as if it were a warm and human heart. The last thing I saw were the remote stars, their fires looking frozen as they came through the window on that snow-crackling night, their light twisted into the shape of a Cross.

III

Christmas: The Woman's Holiday

The Fourth of July was a man's holiday, loud, defiant, full of risk and explosion. The music was brass bands, martial and blaring. As some men were shooting off miniature cannon with a metallic roar, other men were hanging onto terrified horses; I remember the animals whinnying in fright and the men yelling at them in rage. The women did little to get ready for the Fourth, except pray that it would end rapidly and safely.

Christmas was a woman's holiday, quiet, sharing, full of cheer and generosity. The music was bright carols, which seemed to glow out of the singing mouths. As some women were stitching on skirts or crocheting odd, useless things, others were baking in the kitchen; I remember the wood-burning range, its fire humming a lively tune like a primitive carol which had warmed early Christians hiding out in their caves. As the kettles bubbled and the oven temperature rose higher, the air of that kitchen turned as crisp, flaky, and sweet-smelling as fresh bread.

Women began to get ready for Christmas many months in advance. In mother's case, our Christmas always began on the day after Christmas, when she would take me downtown to a store and open her "Christmas Club" for the next year. Her weekly contribution might be only a quarter or a half dollar, but it was her first concern and she would squeeze it out of the little she spent on groceries if need be. Of course, that club was a great thing in my life, for it meant that every week in the year we were reminded of the season of sharing. In the sultry August heat of our Iowa "dog days" we would go down and make our little celebration of the seriousness with which we believed in the holiday to come with the snow and the freezing winds out of the high western plains.

What brought the Holy Family to Bethlehem was a money matter; Joseph had to pay taxes in the town assigned to his tribe. The trip had to be made, and in winter, whether his wife was about to have a child or not. So it was that our tiny money affair of the club brought us into touch with the anticipation of Christmas; winter or summer, mother had to make that trip and pay her own little money offering. It was the happiest thing she did every week.

Why should Christmas not have been the most womanly of all celebrations? It was a day of praise for woman's most desirable and unique aspect: birth. In the dead season came life.

Feeling this appropriateness, women labored to make the day meaningful. By the first frost mother would have us out gathering nuts, the rich and oily black walnut, the crisp brown hazel, the sweet white hickory, and the mellow butternut. From then until December 25 it was all sewing and baking and storing up and hiding away and planning, all of these being acts most congenial to women. In those days of few household appliances a woman with children and without any help put in a long, hard, laboring day. To that was then added all the extra Christmas thought and work. How did mother stand the grind of it? I can only assume that, to a sturdy farm unbringing, there was added a sturdy spirit uplifting.

IV

Christmas: Our Mother's Hands

The sharpest memory of our old-fashioned Christmas Eve is my mother's hand making sure that I was settled in bed. Although her fingers moved gently in the dark of that excited night, they scratched my face with their roughness.

Mother had been sewing for months, making useful and sturdy garments for the children, two boys and two girls. With all the baking, shopping and decorating she had to do, it was natural for her to fall behind in the last days before Christmas. That meant sewing not only late at night but also rapidly. Since much of it was done by hand, she would stab her fingers with the needle, making them a little torn and rough. Some years, the first Christmas red I saw would be a drop of blood at the tip of mother's finger.

All evening I would fight sleep, as if it were a dark angel come to take me out of that bright world where real wax candles burned and wavered dangerously on the tree. The house would be almost loud with the tantalizing smells of things baking, boiling, frying, bubbling on the stove. The sweet of maple sugar blended with the sour of vinegar in a single odor, like a child's gay-sad cry.

If I went to sleep, wasn't there a good chance that I might wake up to find that the whole glittering night had been imagined, and it would just be an ordinary winter day with the drifted sidewalks to shovel? So I became an active nuisance, stealing cookies, pestering my sisters (one older, one younger) at their sewing, and hovering on the edge of mother's bustling activity.

All evening mother would run—literally, for there was no time in those last few hours to walk—from sewing machine to kitchen, whirring at the machine and stirring at the stove. Between these two mechanisms she would do small bits of hand sewing, and these were the loveliest moments of all. She had a small rocking chair, perhaps no more than two thirds of a full-sized rocker. Underneath it was a drawer which swung out to the right, containing tiny compartments for scissors and thimbles, with little pegs on which spools of thread rotated, and colorful pincushions shaped like green frogs or yellow pumpkins. One pincushion was a large strawberry from which hung by a green string a little strawberry with tiny green leaves. The small berry was filled with powdered emery, and mother would plunge a needle rapidly back and forth in it to clean and sharpen the point.

Always in motion, she would rock steadily while doing the fine stitches on my sister's skirt or an embroidered blouse for a cousin or a coat for me. Swiftly, swiftly the point of the needle would leap, as quick and sharp as the points of light in her eyes, and then suddenly it would make a wrong jump and stab a finger. Mother would call out, "Darn! even if I do say it." Her cry would not be in pain, but in distress because the pace of her work would be slowed down just when she was hurrying her fastest.

The break would be a bad one for me, too, since she usually saw me sitting there yawning on the floor, and said, "Up to bed, now, or you won't have time to come down in the morning." I would drag grimly off, and even in bed would force myself to stay awake guessing what the downstairs noises meant, for once again the sewing machine would start its unsteady rush. It was an old foot-treadle type which mother could speed up or slow down by her nimble feet.

Sometimes the rush of sewing would stop and I could hear mother's urgent step running to put still another finished present under the tree, or take from the oven that wonderful bread she made only at Christmas, with raisins, quince, black walnut and hickory nuts inside, and a glaze of cinnamon and brown sugar on the outside. Or the steps would be only a few, and then I would hear the solid, oak rocking of the little chair as she sewed the fine and durable stitches. Next morning I would see in my new shirt the rhythmical pattern of that rocking worked out by her steady needle and her punished fingers and her child-loving heart.

Then would come the time when her steps climbed up to my bedroom and in the black cold of the un-heated room I waited for the old, familiar sound—the creak as her foot hit the fifth tread from the top, which always bent and groaned a little. Then her rush across the floor and her warm hand scratching back and forth over my forehead. That rough hand was more reassuring than a smooth one, for it meant that the good Christmas activity had been going on long enough to break the skin. That hand was a proper part of the season, having made its own tiny blood sacrifice to the holiday.

Lulled by that rough and patient touch, I would sleep, impatient for the morning and its gifts of love and work.

No matter how late she had gone to bed, mother was always up before the rest of us. Waking to the red sun burning like a great candle behind the frost trees on the window, I would creep farther down under the blankets for an instinctive instant. But then, hearing mother's quick spoon beating the buckwheat batter for our breakfast pancakes, knocking against the yellow bowl with a rhythmical repetition of all those hard "b" sounds, I would know that the most beautiful morning of the year had begun. As most of our days began, and ended, with mother making cheerful and useful noises for her family, it was especially right that Christmas should begin that way.

By the time my feet hit the icy floor and had reached the stairway, my brother and sisters would already be floating through space from the top step to the bottom in what seemed, from above, one long glide. Below, we would face the two glowing wonders of Christmas: the tree, all its many-colored candles lit, the tiny flames leaping upward to the homemade star gleaming with its candy-bar and chewing-tobacco leadfoil, and our mother, standing in the kitchen doorway, stirring the dark batter, her face glowing with the heat of cooking and with her excitement at our excitement.

In the kitchen our father would already be attacking the first batch of pancakes before going off to work at six o'clock, as he did every morning of the year. Under the tree would drift a white swirl of packages, most of them made right there in the next room. We were a poor family. Mother and father worked long, hard, twelve-hour days. Christmas was always honored by their practical skills, their quiet belief in labor, and their devotion to us.

Were ever children so lucky?

V

Christmas: The Female Relatives

Whether we had Christmas dinner at our house in town or at the family farm in the country, where mother had been born, made no difference to the women, for they all pitched in and worked no matter whose house it was. That was the woman's way.

There was Aunt Minnie, in whom everything was narrow save her heart. A harsher age would have called her "skinny." Her skin was paper-thin, so that the veins seemed to be on the outside; her body was so slender it looked as if light would pass through it. Her fingers gripping the back of a chair seemed not like hands holding but like wild grape tendrils growing around it. She moved in a tenuous way, abruptly, by jerks, as if not sure that whatever direction she had taken was the right one. Yet she crossed a room faster than any of us, her feet always a little above the floor.

Minnie had a taste for bright colors, so that her dresses would be a slender glory of pink or robin's-egg blue; her rapid motions made her clothing rustle more than other women's, so that I was entranced, when she rushed by with a hot dish, by the gay silken rustle of her gait, with a slight click of bones from her busy skeleton almost audible to my enthusiastic ear. Minnie had a sharp-edged voice which, my father stated with the authority of a man experienced in splitting wood, "would go through an oak chunk." She also rejoiced in a pair of eyes blue as the pulsing vein in her throat, and a nose pointed as a whittled stick.

Crowning Minnie's transparent angularity was a vast head of hair, tumbling and writhing. She always had it carefully shaped and held in place by elaborate braided lengths and fancy pins, so that, from a distance, she seemed to be wearing a hat of strange size and texture.

Minnie's principles of conduct were as narrow as her figure. No man who smoked or drank should go to church, because his defiled voice was obviously unfit to utter the name of the Lord. Her favorite description of a rude boy was "a limb of Satan" (Minnie never spoke the vulgar word "leg"). Grapes, God's original bottles, were meant to be consumed with their lovely juice unchanged by reckless men. In her mind there was no distinction between a person who took an occasional glass of wine and a confirmed drunkard. Both were guilty of corrupting nature. As for tobacco, Minnie had an unarguable explanation: If the Almighty had wanted smoke coming out of the human nose, He would have given Adam a smoke organ to replace that missing rib.

Just as dogs can hear sounds too high for the ordinary ear, so could Minnie smell sins too subtle for the ordinary nose. When the males of our Christmas group had discreetly slipped away to the barn on the grounds of feeding the horses (for the third time that morning!),

46

Minnie would turn the nimble tip of her nose toward the kitchen window facing the barn and sniff the accusing air. The odor of wickedness came riding to her over the strawstack and through the frosted window glass. "They're up to no good out there," she would lament. Sure enough, when the men came back they would have the stare of guilt over their reddened faces and their unnatural laughs still going on over some forbidden joke.

Minnie's prime object of decoration was an enchanting cameo which she wore as a brooch at her neck. The background was blue and the figures were pink. This was fortunate, since around the two discreet heads in the center (a man and a woman gazing fondly but decently at each other) was a row of tiny cherubs, cheerfully naked and gaily pink-bottomed. This was an unexpected exuberance in Minnie, who explained the fleshly display by saying that they were just innocent babes. May I be forgiven my sin in speculating that the innocent babes had any connection with the romantic man and woman of the cameo's center.

For all of her slenderness, Minnie always brought the fattest basket. Having no children, she had no anxieties about the very young needing to protect its teeth and its digestion, so she would give us fruit cakes swollen with exotic dates and spices, candies which she had made in elaborate shapes and exciting colors. She also knit, tatted, crocheted, embroidered and appliquéd, so that her basket was crammed with remarkable and grotesque examples of her skill and fancy.

Impressed as I was with Aunt Minnie, my favorite

was Aunt Lydia (pronounced lid-ee), who worried less about sin and more about hungry children getting fed. "I know all about boys," she would say, slapping yet another helping onto my plate. Then I thought she meant just the holes in our ravenous stomachs, but now, recalling Lydia's lively eye and in the suspicious wisdom of years, I am convinced that she meant quite literally *all*.

If too many revolting suggestions about the boys helping with the kitchen work were made, it was Lydia who would quickly invent errands outside to the milkhouse or the barn or the woodpile, so that we could do tasks worthy of men. It was Lydia who had the figure of attractive neatness, round and medium and supple. It was surprising how she kept it, because her idea of an inadequate meal was one which offered only a single variety of pie, instead of the mince, apple, pumpkin, and cherry which she always made for Christmas. Perhaps she ran off the danger of excess weight by the speed with which she kept the kitchen in a turmoil of everything being cooked at once.

It was also Lydia who saw to it that the children, although put at a special small table at the far end of the room, were a part of the celebration. There was a particular grace which she taught us. On the wonderful Christmas when I said it, there was a special feeling of virtue and power as I looked down the long row of adults with their heads bent waiting to hear *my* voice. I knew that, eager as they were for food, they would wait patiently until I had spoken the grace, and my silence told them that the dedicating moment was over and they could now nourish the body, having nourished the spirit. I must admit, to my shame, that even as I spoke the reverent words I found one eye peering over the table from my bowed head, locating the white meat of turkey on the platter. Of course it looked against my will, but somehow I was not able to stop it. Here is the grace:

> *Lord Jesus, once*
> *A little Child,*
> *Help me to be*
> *A worthy child.*
>
> *Blessèd Jesus,*
> *Hear our call,*
> *Bless this food,*
> *And bless us all.*
>
> *Lord Jesus, come*
> *To us and give*
> *The bread of life*
> *So we may live.*
>
> *Come nourish us*
> *With bread and spirit.*
> *This is our prayer.*
> *We pray you hear it.*

The instant activity which the end of my grace released was not any reluctance to hear solemn words, but just the natural zeal for food by men and women who had worked all morning to that end. The Lord was praised for His bounty by the devotion shown to it.

The bread of life named in the grace had a particular meaning. Modern, store-bought bread was a rage of Uncle Ben's. He would take a loaf of it between his hands and crush it together until it was only as thick as one slice of Aunt Lydia's bread baked in the old Smoke Eater oven with a live flame of oak running across the top under the great cast-iron slab. That bread would sustain life, and Uncle Ben's vigorous paunch proved that it would, as Ben said, "stick by a man."

With all the cousins there, one child was nearly always ill. After dinner the women would gather around the poke and probe and guess in the vague way of the times. No matter what the disorder or the part of the body where it was to be found, Aunt Lydia would rub the afflicted area and then announce that the sure cure was "grandma's grease." This was a liniment whose formula had been passed down in the family for generations. Its basic ingredient was goose fat rendered down with mysterious aromatics and penetrating drugs. It would be warmed on a corner of the stove; then applied briskly, with a woman's calloused hand, it would warm and relieve head, chest, or stomach. More than that, with a soft flannel laid on, the patient would reek gloriously of wild herbs and tame goose.

It was a holiday when women were in charge. They had worked for it, had cooked for it, and given it the fine, feminine quality which Christmas should have, and they ended it. Children were ordered into coats (hills and valleys of depressing pans and dishes having long since been washed while the men napped), the handi-work of each as shown in gifts was praised a final time, and off the various families went, Aunt Lydia neatly tucked in beside Uncle Ben, Aunt Minnie sniffing the clean air anxiously. She did not need to worry. In that hour of celebration and departure, in that wide mid-western landscape, as serene as the wide sky above, there was no hint or chance of evil. The women were in charge.